Libby went to the store.

She got a new flute.

She can play the flute and skip

around her room.

Around and around the room she skips.

2

She pokes her dog, Brute.

"Look at me, Brute.

Look at me skip and play the flute.

Don't I look cute?"

Brute does not think Libby is cute.

Brute thinks she is rude.

Brute wants to take his nap.

Brute jumps up and bites the flute.

He runs out of the room.

"Stop, Brute, stop!" yells Libby.

Brute runs fast!

He runs to his doghouse and

hides the flute.

Now Brute can take his nap!

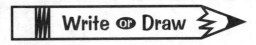

What wakes you up when
you are trying to sleep?